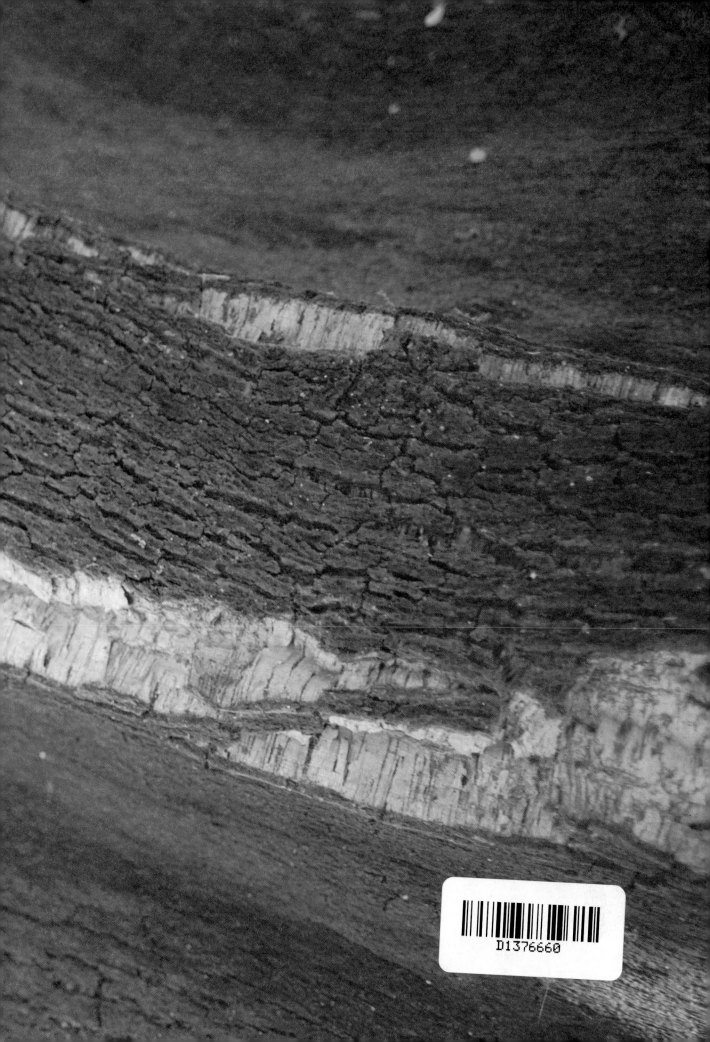

THE CORK

THE CORK

MANUEL ALVES DE OLIVEIRA

LEONEL DE OLIVEIRA

Text:
MANUEL ALVES DE OLIVEIRA

Produced by:
LEONEL DE OLIVEIRA
and
THE RESOURCE AND MARKETING OFFICE
OF GRUPO AMORIM

Design:
FERNANDO ROCHINHA DIOGO
and
ANTÓNIO ROCHINHA DIOGO

Translation:
Communicate Language Institute

Photos:
A. SEQUEIRA
JOÃO FRANCISCO VILHENA
MAURÍCIO ABREU
PENAGUIÃO & BURNAY

Colour Selection:
CONTRATIPO, Lda.

Typeset by Fotocompográfica, Lda.
Printed and bound in March 1994
by Tilgráfica, SA
Portugal

Depósito legal n.º 49 983/91
ISBN 972-95525-0-9

Reviewed and edited for distribution in the United
States and Canada by Portuguese Trade Commission and
the Cork Institute of America and cooperation and
authorization of Amorim Group.

Investimentos, Comércio e Turismo de Portugal

CORK INSTITUTE OF AMERICA

The cork trees are dreaming
their strange wild dreams,
which only the shepherds
and the stones can imagine.

They dream that they are free
and wandering over the earth,
with their roots in the water
and their hair flowing loose.

In the unploughed sky
the clouds are thistles
and the sun is a hawk
which gouges out eyes.

All that is left of dreams
is the insolence of pain.
The pain is real.
The dreams are shadows.

Bound to the earth
by talons of bronze,
the cork trees are dreaming
of impossible destinies.

Armindo Rodrigues,
(The World fits into every Moment) 1945

INTRODUCTION

Unmistakable fruit of the land, the protective and miraculous presence of a traditional livelihood, an ancient tree where the memories and toil of peoples meet — its shadow hugs the contours of an unchanging landscape, rolling down gentle slopes into silent planes and distant valleys beneath southern skies.

The cork oak is one of the essential features of our landscape, our heritage, and our memory of the land — it has shared in the daily life of peoples who learnt to love and nurture it, preparing it over years and years for the final, periodic harvest, its unique gift to the comfort of mankind.

Therein lies its grandeur. Wedding utility with creativity, its unique characteristics have won their place in the history of everyday objects. A tree which shares in the history of this in the far west of Europe, whence it set sail as ambassador of ancient wisdom and where today it is worked with intricate and exacting skill. This is its magic, and its meaning.

In all this, there is one, unique, task in view... the production of cork. A task which demands skills and knowledge from deep in Portuguese memory. The extraction, preparation and finishing of cork exemplifies the close link between man and the land where he was born, his patience and care in tending the tree, a wealth not to be wasted. From the communion of man and nature, the life of the land and the life of man, cork as a product takes its place in the natural, ecological and economic heritage of Portugal.

With care and attention, respect for nature is repaid by her best fruits. The production of cork is undoubtedly an example of the living integration of a fascinating industry in the cycle of nature and the land. This makes it a rare skill, slow and tender, one which survives and accompanies the life of entire generations who, from contact with the land, have known the taste of a relationship of respect and fellowship.

PORTUGAL, THE CORK OAK'S ADOPTED HOME

Portugal may be famed for the Discoveries, but the potential of cork and its practical uses were discovered elsewhere. Cork is the only product in which Portugal currently leads the world, both in production and industrial application. But a long story lies behind this success.

The potential of cork was not discovered in Portugal...

Cork is the name given to the suberose parenchyma, or bark, of the cork oak, a tree of the beech family characteristic of western Mediterranean countries.

Strangely enough, the first peoples to put cork to what became its traditional uses lived in the eastern Mediterranean.

In Egypt, tombs dating back thousands of years were found to contain amphorae with cork stoppers.

In ancient Greece, the bark of the cork oak was used to make buoys to float fishing nets, sandals and the stoppers for vessels for wine and olive oil. The Greek philosopher Teophrasto (IV-III century BC) discovered that once cork was stripped from the tree, a new sheath of better quality quickly formed.

A *TARRO*, TRADITIONAL LUNCH BOX OF FARM WORKERS IN THE ALENTEJO.

With the Romans, cork was put to a wider range of uses. The scholar Marcus Terentius Varron (116 - 27 BC) and the farmer Lúcio Columela (I century) recommended making beehives out of cork, because of its low heat conduction. Gaius Pliny the Elder (c. 23 - 79) referred to roofs of cork-wood plank, a tradition which has persisted in areas of North Africa to this day, and listed the uses of cork oak bark to float anchor ropes or fishing nets, to seal vessels and to produce women's shoes for the winter. Fishermen also used cork to fashion life jackets.

ABOVE: CORK BEEHIVE, OR *CORTIÇO,* USED TO THIS DAY IN BEEKEEPING.

LEFT: FISHING NETS WITH CORK BUOYS. MUSEU DO MAR, CASCAIS.

RIGHT AND LEFT:
TWO ROOMS
LINED WITH CORK
AT THE
CONVENTO DOS
CAPUCHOS,
SINTRA
(XVI CENTURY).

Dioscorides, the second century Greek doctor, gives medicinal uses of the suberose tissue of the cork oak. One of his recipes states that "charred cork rubbed on bald patches with laurel sap makes the hair grow again, thicker and darker than before".

The great step forwards for the generalised use of cork was taken by the French benedictine Dom Pierre Pérignon (1639 - -1715), proctor of the Abbey of Hautvillers, near Epernay (Champagne), to whom the process of champagne production is ascribed. He observed that the wooden stoppers wrapped in hemp soaked in olive oil used for the containers holding sparkling wine often jumped out. He swapped the conical plugs for cork stoppers with surprising results and cork soon came to be essential for wine bottling. It was adopted by wine producers such as Ruinart in 1729 and Moët et Chandon in 1743.

All the evidence points to the first cork used to make stoppers in France came from the Landes, Var and the eastern Pyrenees. Demand for cork and the expansion of the wine

trade, now that quality could be guaranteed, soon sent ripples into neighbouring Catalonia. As a result, in around 1750, in the small town of Angullane, in the province of Gerona, close to the French border, the first cork stopper factory opened, marking the beginning of the industrial application of cork. Production boomed as from the XIX century when bottles took the place of traditional barrels, used since the Romans, to conserve wine.

The replacement of corks by other stoppers, either cheaper or simply more eye-catching, had a serious effect on the cork industry, condemned only to be able to use 25% of the raw-material, a fact which in turn dampened interest in cork oak farming. But all this changed in 1891 when an American by the name of John Smith found it was possible to produce agglomerated cork. A new world of opportunities opened up, in which waste cork from the stopper industry and cork previously thought to be of no commercial value could also be used.

LEFT: MANUELINE WINDOW AT THE CONVENTO DE CRISTO IN TOMAR, DEPICTING CORK IN FISHING TACKLE.

ABOVE: CORK RAFTS, KNOWN AS *CORTIÇOS*, IN A-VER-O-MAR.

... But Portugal has used cork since the founding of the nation

The oldest cork oak fossil found in Portugal is from the Tagus hydrographic basin. This fragment, whose structure is perfectly preserved, is in all respects identical to the trunks of present-day cork oaks. Its age has been calculated at around 10 million years.

Tools fashioned for cork have been preserved from the era of Roman occupation. Cork artefacts are, by their very nature, indestructible. The absence, therefore, of any significant examples surviving from the period following the Roman occupation through to the XII century suggests that, although flourishing on Portuguese soil from time immemorial, cork oaks were rarely exploited during this period.

Later, in the early days of Portuguese nationhood, cork is known to have been used in building (including shipbuilding) and acorns as feed for pigs. References to the protection of acorn production date back as far as the Costumes de Castelo Rodrigo e Castelo Melhor (1209).

By the XIV century the cork oak was an economic asset of national importance, in recognition of which laws were passed to protect cork oak forests. Cork was first exported to England in around 1307 during the reign of Dom Dinis. In 1320 the king took tough measures against anyone damaging "my cork oaks... which stand split and splintered". During the reign of Dom Fernando, cork was one of the main exports to sail out of the port of Lisbon.

From the XIV to the XV century cork gained in importance. In 1456 a foreign merchant was granted a ten-year trade monopoly. But the representatives of the people at the court of Lisbon were not slow to protest against this privilege. Their first complaint in 1459 went unheard, but they kept up their pressure at the courts of 1481-82, 1490 and 1492 and finally, in 1498, won round Dom Manuel, who declared that the cork contracts would be allowed to expire and would not be renewed.

ILLUMINATION IN THE *LIVRO DE HORAS DE D. MANUEL*. THE MAIN SUBJECT IS CORK OAKS BEING SHAKEN; THE ACORNS ARE FED TO PIGS. DEEP CUTS CAN BE SEEN ON THE TREES WHERE THE CORK HAS BEEN EXTRACTED.

COLLECTION AND
TRANSPORT OF
CORK IN THE
THIRTIES.

As the Discoveries gathered momentum, corkwood was used on the most vulnerable parts of ships and caravels. Corkwood was found to be the best choice for the rigging: it was durable and would not rot in water. The *Comentários* de Afonso de Albuquerque speak of "cork ships". Cork was also used for buoys, benches, chests, trunks, bowls, vases, dishes, footwear and other domestic utensils.

Cork bark was put to other uses in Portugal: it was used for fishing nets and to keep out the cold and damp. In various convents, it was used to line cell walls and ceilings, as can be seen at the Convento dos Capuchos in Sintra and the Convento dos Carmelitas in Buçaco.

The evident popularity enjoyed by the cork oak in XV-XVI century Portugal is reflected in the abundance of cork oak motifs on tomb stones, pulpit and altar plinths, in the decoration of frontons and gardens, on the capitals and arches of cloisters, etc. Both the *Livro de Horas de D. Manuel* and the famous window at the Convento de Cristo in Tomar bear eloquent witness to this fashion.

Cork stoppers arrived in Portugal in roughly 1700. They were first used in cylindrical bottles in around 1770 in Oporto, allowing the wine to mature slowly in a glass recipient. Stopper production expanded significantly. In 1797 exports of cork stoppers stood at 115,183 and of corkwood planks at 1,331 tons.

But the expansion was shortlived. The manufacture of cork stoppers picked up between 1822 and 1826 with the arrival in Portugal of skilled workmen from Catalonia, bringing with them more advanced techniques. Nonetheless, foreign sales of stoppers in 1831 tallied only around 33,947 gross.

The real boom in the cork industry began in the last quarter of the XIX century. Between 1890 and 1917 the industry's workforce more than doubled, and by 1930 the figure had increased fivefold from the last decade of the XIX century, reaching a total of 10,000 workmen. Portugal had become the world's leading cork producer.

LOADING CORK CARGO IN THE THIRTIES.

Today the cork oak's adopted home

Portugal is a land of forests. Of the 88,705 km² of mainland Portugal, more than one third is forested.

The cork oak is one of the country's main forest species. Covering 660,000 hectares (22%), it is second only to the pine (1,249,00 hectares, 40%). The holm oak and the eucalyptus occupy 464,000 hectares (15%) and 435,000 hectares (14%) respectively. The remaining 280,000 hectares (9%) of Portugal's forests are occupied by a variety of other species.

Thanks to the cork oak, Portugal is the world leader in the cork industry, producing more and better than any of its competitors, and boasting the largest industrial and marketing structure.

Because of particular climatic conditions — temperature, light, rainfall — the cork oak established itself in the Western part of the Mediterranean basin. It is found in the north of Africa (Morocco, Algeria and Tunisia), in southern France (especially Corsica), Italy, Spain and, above all, in Portugal,

THE FIRST
FACILITIES
RELONGING TO
ANTÓNIO ALVES
AMORIM (1870).

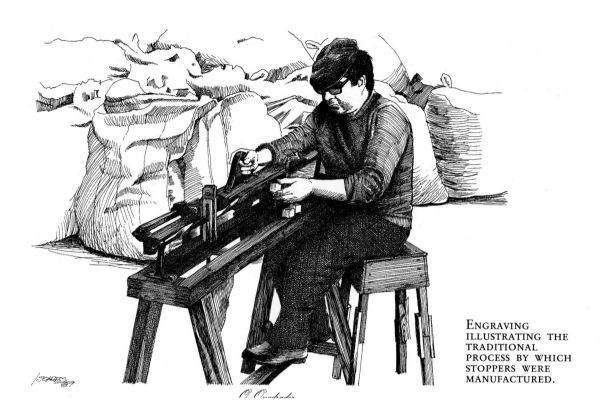

ENGRAVING
ILLUSTRATING THE
TRADITIONAL
PROCESS BY WHICH
STOPPERS WERE
MANUFACTURED.

DISTRIBUTION OF
CORK FORESTS IN
THE
MEDITERRANEAN
BASIN.
NOTE THAT THE
AREA WHERE THE
CORK OAK GROWS
OVERLAPS WITH A
MAJOR WINE
PRODUCING AREA.

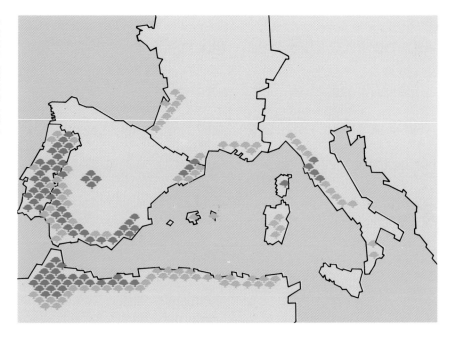

which has become its adopted homeland. Worldwide, the cork oak covers 2.2 million hectares, of which 660,000 hectares (30%) are in Portugal, 460,000 hectares (21%) in Algeria, 440,000 hectares (20%) in Spain, 350,000 hectares (16%) in Morocco, 110,000 hectares (5%) in France and 90,000 hectares in (4%) in both Italy and Tunisia.

It is interesting to note that the area of cork oak forest in Portugal in 1915 stood somewhere between 300,000 and 472,000 hectares.

Although Portugal has only 30% of the world's cork oaks, the country accounts for more than half of the world's cork production. Today's figures show Portugal with an annual production of 170,000 tonnes (average of the last nine years), as against 65,000 tonnes (18.8%) in Spain, 27,000 tonnes (7.8%) in Algeria, 26,000 tonnes (7.5%) in Morocco and 13,000 tonnes (3.7%) in France.

The cork oak grows in sandy chalk-free soils, with low nitrogen and phosphorus levels, but rich in potassium and with a pH of between 5 and 6. Ideal conditions include rainfall of between 400 and 800 millimetres a year, temperatures which never fall below -5 °C and an altitude of between 100 and 300 metres.

These requirements are met in a narrow band around the western coast of the Mediterranean. Cork oaks are not found to the east of the Ionian Sea, Sicily and Calabria being considered their eastern frontier. To the south, the species does not reach the 44th parallel, although in Morocco it goes beyond the 34th parallel. To the north it reaches as far as the 44th parallel in the Var and the Landes, in France. To the west lies a stretch of cork oak along the Atlantic, covering a good part of the Iberian peninsula and a considerable area of Morocco, down as far as the 32nd parallel.

In *Portugal,* the cork oak is in its element. Of all the trees in the country, it is the most evenly distributed and can be found even in the cold, inhospitable clime of Trás-os-Montes. Nonetheless, the climate and multiple other circumstances, which favour or disfavour the growth of cork oak forests, have endowed a mere five districts of the centre and south — Beja, Évora, Portalegre, Santarém and Setúbal — with 87% of the country's total cork oak cover.

LOCATION OF CORK OAK CULTIVATION IN PORTUGAL.

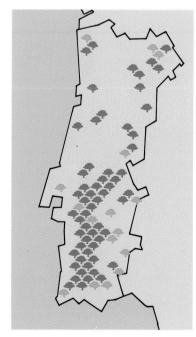

In *Spain*, the cork oak occupies vast tracts of the provinces of Badajoz, Cáceres, Cadiz, Huelva, Málaga and Seville. However, methodical exploitation of the cork oak in Spain started in Catalonia, in 1790. But in the first half of the nineteenth century alone, Catalonia's cork oak forests were reduced by 45% and have never recovered.

In *Algeria*, a strip of cork oak forests penetrating 60 to 70 kilometres inland skirts the coast for a distance of 450 kilometres between Algiers and Cape Roux (continuing a further 150 kilometres into Tunisia as far as the environs of Bizerta). Owing to peculiar climatic conditions, the cork oak in Algeria grows at altitudes of up to 1,550 metres. On the other hand, it is not found anywhere further than 100 kilometres inland.

In *Morocco*, the cork oak flourishes along the entire Medi-

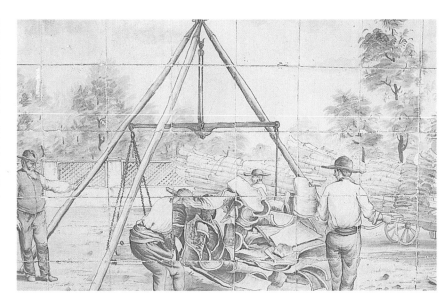

terranean coast and along the Atlantic coast as far as Marra-kech, and in the south of the country can be found at altitu-des as high as 2,200 metres. The most outstanding of Morrocan cork oak stands is that around Mamora, with an area of 136,000 hectares, which, in the second decade of this century provided feeding grounds for 500,000 heads of cattle and 100,000 heads of sheep and goats.

In *France*, the most valuable area of cork oak forest is found in the Var, where the species occupies a coastal strip 100 metres in length between Toulon and Cannes. Corsica can also boast flourishing cork forests in the districts of Sartè-ne (in the south) and Ajaccio (in the east) and on the eastern coast from Cap Corse.

Italy has made little of the potential of the cork oak resour-ces in Sicily and Sardinia. On the mainland their are small is-lands of cork oaks in Tuscany, Lazio, along the shoreline of the Tyrrhenian as far as Anzio, in the province of Littoria, and in parts of Calabria.

In *Tunisia*, the cork oak forests, a continuation of the strip running along the Algerian coast, reach as far as the environs of Bizerta, a strip 150 kilometres in length. They are concen-

LEFT: PANEL OF AZULEJOS BY GILBERTO RENDA, AT THE RAILWAY STATION IN SANTIAGO DO CACÉM, DEPICTING CORK BEING TRANSPORTED ON CARTS DRAWN BY OXEN.

BELOW: BENCH MADE FROM THREE CORK OAK TRUNKS. MUSEU DA CERÂMICA DAS CALDAS DA RAINHA.

trated in large stands in Nefza-Mogode and Khroumiria (where the forest is divided in three parts).

The growing value of cork has led other countries outside the western Mediterranean basin to try cultivating the cork oak, with little success. These include the Soviet Union, in the Crimea and the subtropical regions of Transcaucasia, the United States of America, whose industry is a significant world cork consumer, in California and other southern states, Japan, where intense research began into this sector in 1933, and Argentina, Australia, Israel, South Africa, Turkey and Uruguay.

The present outlook for the cork industry in Portugal is extremely promising. The country's cork oak forests represent 30% of the world total and Portugal produces more than half of the world's cork. Given that a cork oak produces cork tissue until it is 150 or even 200 years old, during which time it may be stripped 15 to 18 times, and that the average ages of trees presently in production is 85 years and that the area under plantation is growing by an average of 4% a year, cork production can look forward to a rosy future in Portugal.

Cork production in Portugal has grown spectacularly this century. In 1921, annual production averaged around 16,000

tonnes. Production then climbed steeply: reaching 41,000 tonnes in 1927 and 90,000 tonnes in 1934. Today, annual output has stabilised at around 170,000 tonnes, more than half of the world's total production.

Even more spectacular has been the growth in Portugal of the cork processing industry. In 1925, 90% of cork production (60,000 tonnes) underwent no significant industrial processing in the country.

Two factors had a decisive influence on subsequent investment; the Spanish Civil War and the armed conflict in Algeria. In the latter country alone, the area of degenerate cork forest in 1977 (285,000 ha) exceeded the area of productive forest, explaining the low average productivity per hectare.

In the first half of the century, the world cork market was controlled by a handful of multinationals. However, their productive investment was minimal, especially in Portugal and Spain. Their only presence in our country was through small offices which acted as purchasing centres for the raw material and for some manufactured goods which were channelled to other centres for processing and distribution.

It was in the 1960s that Portuguese companies started to put money into modern factories and verticalizing the industry.

Today, the Portuguese cork industry not only processes almost all the country's production but also imports cork, and manufactures 70% of the world's cork products.

There are at present more than 600 industrial facilities operating in Portugal, employing a labour force of about 15,000.

The Aveiro district alone is home to 72% of factories in operation. The districts of Aveiro, Setúbal, Faro and Évora between them account for around 96%.

Cork products were exported in 1990 to the tune of 80,433,356,000 escudos (corresponding to 105,516 tonnes). Imports of cork in the same year amounted to 8,141,580,000 escudos (23,859 tonnes).

THE CORK OAK.
PAINTING BY
DÓRDIO GOMES.
CENTRO DE ARTE
MODERNA,
FUNDAÇÃO
CALOUSTE
GULBENKIAN,
LISBON.

In the same period natural cork stoppers accounted for 55% of total cork product exports. At 44,614,694,000 escudos, this trade is worth more than the export of Port Wine.

With special laws for its defence

The first known reference to the cork oak in law dates from 1209, in the Costumes e Foros de Castelo Rodrigo, a measure taken in protection of acorns. A fine of one morabitino was payable by "anyone who shakes oak trees with a stick".

Other legislation was added down the centuries to protect the country's forest resources against damage from fire, livestock or felling.

In the present century, Portugal not only took wider ranging measures to protect the cork oak than any other country, but also led the world in outlawing exploitative practices in corkwood farming, setting regulations for thinning, pruning and stripping the cork bark.

Current legislation on cork oak cultivation covers four major areas: forest land, the cork oak, cork and the cork oak farmer.

INSTRUCTIONS ISSUED BY THE FORESTRY COMMISSION ON PRUNING CORK OAKS.

PROTECTION OF FOREST LAND

Decree no.13658, dated 20 May 1927, prohibits agricultural cultivation between the trees of oak groves on hillside locations or above water courses, or where tilling or ploughing the soil might loosen it unduly.

The same decree lays down the legal procedure to be followed should the farmer wish to convert the land from silviculture to agricultural production.

This procedure includes an inspection, and a further decree, of 25 November 1930, requires the farmer to notify the local offices of the Inland Revenue, for the change to be re-corded on the Land Registry.

PROTECTION OF THE CORK OAK

The cork oak is protected, from the moment of germina-tion until overcome by old age, which no human law can pre-vent.

The felling of cork oaks, other than in essential thinning operations or of trees evidently too old for productive purpo-ses, is punishable by a fine. Breach of this regulation is consi-dered an indictable offence (délit), under the terms of a de-cree of 21 April 1931.

Under the law of 20 May 1927, a special licence is required to convert land from forestry to agricultural use, or to a diffe-rent form of forestry, to fell trees systematically or even to cut or pull up stumps when the grove may be proved to have been attacked by parasitic diseases.

The same law requires the owners of woods and forests to take preventive measures and to combat pests and diseases when so instructed by the regional forestry officials.

A fine was also established for any farmer wishing to clear his land by fire without giving neighbouring landow-ners one week's notice to take suitable steps against the fire spreading.

The same decree provides for defence against damage by goat herds. A landowner or tenant farmer may only keep free-grazing goats if he has enough pasture land at his dispo-sal; he must apply for a licence from the local council, which needs to be renewed annually.

Thinning productive or sapling cork oaks is only permitted if the normal density of the community is not disrupted. This law, dating from 24 June 1934, requires the forester to notify the Forestry Commission (Direcção-Geral dos Serviços Flo-

INSTRUCTIONS ISSUED BY THE FORESTRY COMMISSION ON STRIPPING CORK OAKS.

restais e Aquícolas) fifteen days before commencing the operation. The commission may send an inspector to change the technique or the intensity of thinning, or even prohibit the operation.

A decree-law issued on 21 April 1931 states that there are no restrictions on pruning cork oaks, provided that no irreversible damage is done to the tree's productive capacity. An earlier law of 25 November 1930, lays down that cork oaks may only be pruned from December to March; shoots and suckers, however, may be removed at any time of year. Once again the Forestry Commission must be given 15 days notice of intention to prune on any property. Any mutilation of cork trees is expressly forbidden.

The legal regulations on cork stripping date from 24 June 1937. Saplings may only be stripped for the first time when the circumference of the trunk around the cork reaches at least 60 centimetres. The first branches may only be stripped when, measuring around the cork-producing or phellogenic layer, a diameter of 15 centimetres or circumference of 47 centimetres is attained. Extraction of reproduction cork (second and subsequent stripping) is expressly prohibited from trees less than 9 years old.

CORK PRODUCTION

Portuguese law protects not only the cork oak. Special attention is also given to the oaks foremost product, cork, in order to maintain standards of quality.

Decree no. 27776, 24 June 1937, prohibits the extraction of reproduction cork from trees younger than 9 years old. The law also covers cork from felled trees less than 9 years old, which may be neither extracted nor traded.

Decree no. 27809 imposes other obligations on both cork producers and the buyers of cork products.

A statistical declaration must be made of cork production, and delivered between 1 October and 31 December.

Buyers of cork oaks from thinning operations and of wood from pruning are required to make a declaration of approximate quantities if they extract the cork, whatever the end use might be.

These declarations must specify separately the quantities of reproduction cork (second and subsequent strippings), summer virgin and winter virgin (from pruning and thinning).

PROTECTION OF THE CORK FARMER

The State guarantees the farmer both technical and financial protection.

Under decree no. 27776, 24 June 1937, farmers may request the Forestry and Agricultural Commission to provide technical assistance to help them with thinning and to improve their farming methods.

Loans to cork producers became widely available and regulated under decrees nos. 18195, 12 April 1930 and 23934, 31 May 1934. These credit facilities remained in place and were subsequently expanded.

In the 1980s, the Portuguese government started a reforestation programme, which included a further 150,000 ha of cork oak cultivation.

With membership of the EEC, the Forestry Action Plan gave a new impetus to cork oak farming, with 100% grants for investments and investment plans. This programme (triennal) went into operation in 1987, reaching an area of 50,700 hectares, 42,000 of which were upgraded and 8,700 were planted from scratch.

The second programme, also running for three years (1990--1992), is the continuation of the first. Both of them subsidise fire-breaks, the felling of old trees and forest pruning.

That so much far-reaching legislation exists to regulate cork production can only come as a surprise to someone innocent of a simple if little known fact: if it is undeniable that Port wine is Portugal's premier agricultural product on world markets, there can similarly be no doubt that cork is one of the most important products for the country's balance of payments and the only product in which Portugal is a major force, indeed the world leader.

THE CORK OAK

The cork oak dates from the Oligocene stage of the Tertiary period, in other words from the time of the formation of the Mediterranean basin, making it one of the youngest quercus species.

In existence, according to some sources, for more than 60 million years, it is found widely represented in European flora since the Oligocene stage.

It is thought likely that it was disseminated from the region now covered by the Tyrrhenian Sea, and that it migrated along the cordillera which linked the lands now submerged by the Aegean Sea and the Iberian Peninsula in the Miocene stage.

The tree

The cork oak is a dicotyledon of the family of the Fagaceae, to which equally familiar trees in Portugal, such as the chestnut and the beech, also belong.

Within this botanical family it is part of the genus *Quercus*. The Quercus genus includes more than 600 species, of which the most typical is the oak. Many of these species are of great economic value because of their wood, inner bark or fruit.

The foremost of these is *Quercus suber L.*, to give it its scientific name, the only quercus species to produce cork. No other tree produces such a thick or resistant bark.

CONSTITUTION

The cork oak is an extremely diverse forest species, appearing in dozens of varieties. These can be distinguished by certain features of their cupules, leaves and fruits.

To study its form we need to look at three components: the roots, trunk and crown.

IMPRESSIVE EXAMPLE OF A CENTURY-OLD CORK OAK, WITH A CROWN MEASURING 28 METRES. IN 1991, THE TREE YIELDED 1,200 KG OF CORK.

When the cork oak acorn germinates it issues a primary root, or radicle, which grows downwards as straight and as deep as the nature of the soil will allow, anchoring the tree. The tap root is later complemented by various secondary, or

strong, muscular boughs, more horizontal than vertical, from which other branches grow profusely.

The crown, when the tree is young, is round, but·in later years spreads wide rather than high. This gives the older trees their majestic, patriarchal mien.

Each bough divides into branches, which successively divide into smaller branches down to twigs covered in foliage with a herbaceous appearance.

The leaves are green. They comprise two parts: an upper part which is smooth and shiny, and a lower part, facing down, which is a light matt colour, covered in down and orifices, the stomata (about 500 to each square millimetre).

Buds develop along every young branch in spring at the points where they are joined to the leaves and at the ends. From these buds spring new branches shoots or flowers.

The leaves generally last two years, although in cool locations they may last as many as three. Only under exceptional circumstances, with a prolonged drought in densely populated communities, or after excessive cork stripping, might a tree lose all or a large part of its foliage during the summer.

Premature leaf abscission, if frequent and accompanied by other symptoms such as dry branches, reduced growth, etc., is a sign that the tree's vitality is in decline.

The cork oak begins to bear fruit when it reaches maturity at the age of around 15 to 20 years.

In Portugal it flowers from April to June, and sometimes into August and September.

The male flowers have a perianth of 4 to 6 petals, green, streaked with vermillion or pink along the margin. They are arranged in long slender catkins, hanging from leaf axils or stipular scales.

The female flowers are protected by a scaly cupule and arranged in short spikes comprising 2 to 5 flowers on the leaf axils on the middle to end part of the year's growth. The ovary is made up of three loculi, each with two ovules. After fer-

CORK OAK TRUNK
WHERE TWO
LEVELS OF CORK
CAN BE SEEN: AT
THE TOP, VIRGIN
CORK, AND
BELOW,
REPRODUCTION
CORK.

tilisation the flowers become uniloculate and uniovulate, and the resulting fruit is general monospermous.

The fruit is an acorn which takes a long time to ripen. Indeed, the acorns in different parts of the tree ripen at different times because of the long flowering period. Towards the end of September and during October the first crop of fruit appears, known in Portuguese as *bastão*, born from flowers formed during the later stages, September and October, of the previous year's growing cycle. The second layer of fruit, a richer and more abundant crop, is known as *lande*, and ripens in November and December after 6 or 7 months of development. The third and final layer yields a tiny fruit, *landisco*, which in cold winters does not always ripen. It is born from flowers fertilised at the end of the normal season, in July and August.

BIRTH AND NOURISHMENT

An acorn which falls to the ground at the end of the autumn or during the winter and germinates sprouts a small shoot, which is the beginning of the root of the young plant.

When the root has developed to a certain point it produces another small shoot with leaves, which is the beginning of the plant's trunk and crown.

The young plant may grow vigorously even if the root is not anchored in the soil; in the early stages it depends for nutrients not on the roots, but on food reserves in the acorn.

Like any living being, the cork oak requires food. This need is met by its roots and leaves.

The thinnest of the roots, known as root hairs, absorb from the soil substances dissolved by water consisting in the most part of mineral salts.

SPONTANEOUS FOREST OF CORK OAK SAPLINGS *(CHAPARROS)*.

This mix of mineral salts and water forms what is known as the xylem sap, channelled up the tree through the ligneous veins to the leaves, which function as suction pumps.

The leaves have a dense network of stomata which are open and allow water to evaporate as vapour, sucking up the xylem sap in an unceasing cycle of permanent intercommunication between roots and leaves.

However, transpiration, or water output to the exterior, is not the only activity found in the leaves. Air enters the leaves from the atmosphere, and the leaf tissue fixes the carbon dioxide, releasing oxygen into the atmosphere.

The carbon dioxide fixed by the leaves is transformed, thanks to photosynthesis, into organic substances or carbohydrates.

These organic substances are mixed with the xylem sap to form the phloem sap which runs down the sieve tubes through the entire plant, from the ends of the leaves to the farthest, finest root hairs.

Circulation in the plant is thus twofold: a rising current of xylem sap through the ligneous veins, from the roots to the leaves, and a downwards current of phloem sap through the sieve tubes, from the leaves to the roots.

Excess food is stored as reserves in different parts of the plant to be used when the need arises.

GROWTH AND DEVELOPMENT

The tree grows in two directions at the same time: in height, or vertically, and in breadth, or horizontally.

Upwards growth proceeds as follows: new branches or flowers grow forth when buds, found at the ends of small branches and at leaf axils, open in the springtime.

The annual growth of each small branch through the terminal buds results in vertical growth of the tree.

The development out from the axil buds fills out the branch structure of the crown.

Horizontal, outward growth proceeds along different lines. In order to understand this process it should be remembered that both the trunk and the boughs of the cork oak comprise three areas: an outer layer (cork), an inner section (xylem) and a layer running between these two, the inner bark.

These three areas are separated by very thin, invisible layers which are responsible for the outward growth of the tree.

The thin layer between the xylem and the inner bark is called the cambium and creates both more xylem and more inner bark.

The layer between the inner bark and the cork is known as the phellogen, whose function is also twofold. It causes the inner bark to grow and, as its Greek name suggests, it generates cork.

It should be noted that the phloem sap circulating in the inner bark not only feeds the tree but also makes it grow, both upwards and out.

Despite being an evergreen, the cork oak does not grow all year round.

During the winter, growth is reduced to a minimum because of the cold. The tree is dormant, and neither xylem nor cork is formed.

The rising temperature in the spring awakens the cork oak and growth restarts, to continue until the first cold days of October.

The cells formed by both the cambium and the phellogen in the burst of spring growth are bigger and have thinner walls, giving both the xylem and the cork a lighter coloured and more supple appearance.

Before the first rains of October, the relative dryness of the soil and the lower temperature make it more difficult for the tree to produce both xylem and phloem sap, reducing growth. Consequently, the cells produced are smaller and have thicker walls. The difference in cork between the spring-summer layer and the autumn layer can easily be seen, marked out by a narrow black line.

TWO CORK OAK
PLANTATIONS
WHERE THE
STRAIGHT LINES
ARE A CLEAR SIGN
OF CONTROLLED
CULTIVATION.

Each year's growth comprises therefore two distinct layers, which can be used to determine the exact age of the cork and of the trunk.

The cork oak also resembles any other living being in that it passes through four main stages from birth to natural death.

Sapling cork oaks, i.e. before reaching adulthood, are known in Portugal as *chaparros*.

During the early stages of growth, the roots of a young sapling are disproportionate to the stem. If sown on permeable ground where the plant may flourish, the primary root may

grow to more than 50 centimetres before the stem reaches 30 centimetres.

At this age the roots are proportionally more extensive than the crown, and the area of root hairs sucking xylem sap from the earth is greater than that of the leaves fixing carbon dioxide from the air. If the soil is rich in mineral salts this disproportion is yet further marked.

Given the space to flourish, the sapling grows with great vigour; the trunk widens out and the crown takes a semispherical form.

The roots, however, will not enjoy the same freedom of

movement. They soon encounter a rocky layer and stop growing downwards to spread outwards instead.

The crown soon catches up with the roots in size and a balance is achieved between the substances taken from the soil
and the quantity of organic compounds formed in the leaves.

When this happens it is a sign that the sapling is now a full
grown oak, having reached its adult state.

The cork and xylem cambium layers slacken their activity
and the annual shoots are shorter; the time has come to flo-
wer and bear fruit.

With the passing years the proud densely branched crown
still has room to grow whereas the roots can grow no further
or can no longer find the mineral salts from the depleted
earth.

The cork oak is consequently the victim of an increasing
imbalance between the amounts of mineral salts and organic
compounds, signalling the onset of old age.

The greater growth of the crown, in disproportion to that of
the roots, whose work becomes laborious with the ever more
impoverished state of the soil, causes the formation of new xylem to slow down, in turn impeding the upward circulation of
xylem sap. At the same time, the debilitated foliage is less resistant to attack from certain plagues and diseases and becomes
weaker still; the tree finds itself deprived of a good part of the
organic products which it needs in order to live.

Old age sets in. Deficiency of mineral salts and carbohydrates makes the leaves turn yellow, new shoots are shorter each
year, and the annual layers of xylem and cork are progressively thinner.

As time passes the ravages of old age bear down heavier,
clearly seen at the ends of the roots which are the first parts
to die and wither to dry stumps.

Finally, after a century or more of doggedly withstanding
the hardships of sun and cold, the onslaughts of the wind and
the poverty of the soil, the cork oak finally succumbs.

Ecological environment

Like any other living organism, the cork oak, in order to flourish and develop all it potential, requires certain basic environmental conditions.

A favourable environment for the cork oak comprises three factors: the soil, the climate and the surrounding vegetation.

The three factors are so closely related that it is difficult to consider them in isolation. Hence the vegetation declines if left unprotected when the climate turns inhospitable and the land unyielding. And the soil deteriorates when the plant cover degenerates leaving the soil exposed and unprotected. Equally, climatic conditions can worsen precisely because of the destruction of the forest layer protecting both vegetation and soil and creating microclimates finely tuned to the development needs of particular plant species.

These three factors, working in harmony, make for not only profitable crops but also satisfactory quality of the cork itself. They are the precise reason why Portugal has become the adoptive home of the cork oak, leading the world in both production and quality.

SOIL

The cork oak is broadly tolerant as to the chemical make--up of the soil, the one exception in Portuguese forest soils being an excess of lime.

In Portugal, the widespread occurrence of the species on the tertiary deposits of the Tagus and Sado hydrographic basins in soils of granite and Pre Cambrian schists, of the archeozoic and lower carboniferous layers, is not so much a symptom of a preference for these types of soil but simply evidence of its capacity to exploit sandy and lime-free soils, which are sometimes utterly destitute and subject to climatic conditions under which no other forest species would survive.

The cork oak is more readily found in areas of Portugal

CORK OAK PLANTATION WITH AREAS OF SAND AS FIREBREAKS.

where the potential for fertility is normally low; the soils are virtually lime-free, the humus content is very slight, nitrogen, phosphoric acid and lime are in short supply, whereas there is potassium aplenty. The soil is light, typically sandy, loose, and poor in soluble substances because of high permeability and reduced capacity to retain water. The land is acid, pH hovering around 4, 5 and 6.

Strictly speaking therefore, the soils of cork woods in Portugal cannot be considered forest soils. But this is no argument against the need for their preservation. On the contrary, conservation of the fertility of the lands where the cork oak flourishes should be one of the prime tasks of cork farming managers.

Over-exploitative cereal farming, because of exclusively chemical fertilisation, clearance of shrubland and undergrowth, intensive grazing, fire clearance, etc., all have negative repercussions on both the vigour of cork oaks and the quantity and quality of cork production.

With an ever smaller content of organic matter in the soil, the pedological conditions deteriorate, the bases are increasingly lost, opening the way for erosion, microbial activity is weakened and sterility and aridity set in irreversibly.

Soil degradation does irreparable damage to the environment needed for cork cultivation. In degenerate soils the cork oak grows more slowly, its vitality and consequently its production is reduced, and it ages more rapidly. When a very high percentage of saplings succumb at only one or two years of age, cork oak growth has practically reached the point of no return.

In general, the cork oak is not very demanding of soil quality, taking exception only to particularly high levels of lime or clay. It is also broadly tolerant of acidity, which can lie anywhere between 4.5 and 7. The ideal pH value for the cork oak has been put at 5.67.

In the Mediterranean area, where it originated, the cork oak is found in soils with a similar geological structure to those of the areas where it has settled in Portugal.

CLIMATE

Altitude, temperature and rainfall are amongst the climatic features of greatest bearing on the cork oak's ecosystem.

Portugal's major cork forests are situated at altitudes of less than 200 metres, in the Tagus and Sado hydrographic basins.

But in the centre and north of the country good tracts of cork oak are to be found at altitudes of 700 metres and even, in the case of the Gerês hills, at between 800 and 900 metres.

If the forest location is sheltered and sunny, as in the Bornes mountains in Trás-os-Montes, the cork oak can feel at home as high as 950 metres above sea level.

It should be noted, however, that only 11.5% of the total area of Portugal lies at more than 700 metres, which of course in no sense stands in the way of a possible and desirable increase in cork oak forestation in the country.

Outside Portugal, the cork oak grows at high altitudes thanks to the low latitudes of these countries.

Turning now to temperature, the cork oak is more sensitive to cold than to heat, and will not endure winter temperatures of below -5 °C, which in Portugal only occur in the mountainous regions of the North and inland Beiras.

The main areas of cork forest in Portugal are found in zones where July isotherms are of the order of 22 to 24 °C, and the January isotherms of the order of 8 to 10 °C. Cork oak specialists regard this as the tree's ideal climate.

Rainfall is a greater determining factor. In principle, it should stand at between 600 and 800 millimetres per annum.

The major centre of cork oak forest in Portugal registers annual precipitation of between 400 and 800 millimetres, and the greater part of this area enjoys between 600 and 800 millimetres.

But more important than the quantity of rainfall is its distribution over the year. This is a factor which may cause different levels of aridity in areas at the same latitude.

The fact that the present distribution of the cork oak in Portugal in areas where the land is considered to be amongst the most unyielding and the climate the most inclement should not lead one to conclude that the species has a clear preference for inhospitable conditions, or to suppose that for cork farming, the worse the better, as far as soil and climate are concerned.

NATURALLY GERMINATED OAK TREE STANDING ALONE BY A SMALL WATER COURSE.

In fact, the cork oak is not particularly inclined to such adverse growing conditions. It is, however, remarkably adaptable to the impositions to which it is subjected; this versatility gives it the structural characteristics of a xerophyte. These

serve it well, allowing it to take advantage of environmental conditions under which the survival of other woody species would be difficult.

VEGETATION

In the absence of accurate knowledge of the flora specific to cork oak communities, it is practically impossible to reconstruct the phytosociology of the cork oak.

Various factors, which may be traced to the intervention, direct or individual, of man, such as low tree density, indiscriminate pruning, undergrowth clearance followed by cereal farming, etc., have all contributed to an alteration of the vegetation which would have accompanied the development of the first, spontaneous cork woods.

Seasonal conditions determined by climatic, edaphic and orographic conditions, affected to a greater or lesser extent by the greater or lesser density of cork oaks, and heavily dependant on human activity, affect the associations of plants which presently cover the ground of cork woods.

Various woody and non-woody plants together with numerous shrub species keep phytosocial company with the cork oak.

In coastal areas, higher rainfall and easier soil conditions encourage a profuse undergrowth of trees and shrubs.

Even in the forests of the Alentejo, worst affected by arable farming, manual clearance of the undergrowth of shrubs and other plants, a kind of plant cover soon reforms, albeit sparse and withering.

One thing, however, is certain. Without proper cover, the soil faces inevitable ruin, and in ruinous soil no plant life can survive, let alone multiply.

The tree stratum creates the right conditions — light, temperature and humidity — for the accumulation of humus, which encourages the settlement of a richer and more varied flora.

The impoverishment and consequent degradation of cork woods is often due to the destruction or serious deterioration of the cork oak's environment. Attacks upon vegetation which gathers spontaneously in the confidence of the continuing company of the cork oak can gravely undermine the profitability/productivity and even the survival of cork oak cultivation.

Moreover, the cork oak, as well as being a species which adapts to soils practically incapable of supporting any other economically viable crop, props up the ecological balance in the inhospitable areas where it grows, preventing their degradation.

Against the threat of desertification in the microclimate south of the Tagus, the cork oak is an inestimable boon. A sturdy and steadfast species, providing a raw material increasingly necessary for the comfort of modern life and for state-of-the-art technology, it has the advantage of providing a relative early return on investment. The yield generated periodically gains in value, in both quantity and quality, over several generations.

Husbandry

Stern, sturdy and unusually resistant, the cork oak makes few demands upon its environment. The same cannot be said when we come to deal with the exploitation of its full economic potential.

The husbandry required by the cork oak may be divided into two areas: care of the soil where it is planted and care of the tree itself.

SOIL TREATMENT

Two measures need to be taken in the area of cork oak woods; sometimes they are alternatives, at other times both are necessary.

Firstly, the soil must be tilled periodically, whether or not cereal crops, characteristic of cork woods, are to be planted. Secondly, the undergrowth must be cleared every 4 or 5 years in cork oak communities under forestry management.

Undergrowth clearance followed by tillage has been shown to bring great benefits to cork oak woods. In addition to the production of cereals, meat and timber, the oaks themselves are revitalised and grow more vigorously, resulting in an increase in the economic value of the cork, whose quality and quantity are both enhanced.

But the benefits of clearing the undergrowth and tilling the

an economic limit to its usefulness, and after a certain age it loses its value.

Thinning is then imperative, but must be conducted judiciously. An overly dense cork oak wood may be prejudicial, but the dangers of under-population are no less considerable.

Ideally, a cork oak settlement will flourish when the soil is completely shaded from the sun by the branches and leaves of the cork oaks.

The choice of trees to fell to the benefit of the others should fall upon diseased or very aged trees, weaker oaks, overcome in the struggle for survival with the surrounding trees, those which produce cork of inferior quality and trees with malformations.

Communities should be thinned every 9 or 10 years; in other words, at a rhythm much the same as that for cork stripping or pruning. It is advisable to proceed with this operation during the period when the oak is growing, so that the best use can be made of the cork, inner bark and wood cleared away.

PRUNING

Circumstances dictate the growth and development of the cork tree. They also determine the husbandry needed for the tree to give of its best economically. Pruning, when practicable, is the prime means of fostering productivity.

Cork oaks are pruned for three different aims, depending on the age and vitality of the tree: training the young tree, maintaining the form and vigour of mature trees and heading back to revitalise aged trees.

The law in Portugal lays down that cork oaks may only be pruned when the tree is dormant, in the winter months from December to March.

All cuts leave a wound of exposed sapwood which, without the protection of the inner bark and cork, is exposed to the ravages of sun and rain and will tend to decay.

THIS PAGE:
YOUNG CORK
OAKS FROM WHICH
CORK WAS
STRIPPED IN 1991,
CORRESPONDING
TO NO. 1.

To minimise this risk, pruning cuts should not be made on thick branches. Tearing the tree fibres should be avoided; a clean cut should be made close to, and flush with, the branch or limb.

Saplings are pruned to give them the best chances of growing to healthy adulthood, in other words, to produce easily extracted optimum quality cork. The aim is a tall, straight trunk, normally between 2 and 3 metres high, on which long, straight cork planks may form. The tree is then

ADULT CORK OAKS FROM WHICH CORK HAS RECENTLY (1991) BEEN STRIPPED.

pruned to train 2 to 4 boughs branching off from the trunk, similarly long and smooth, capable of producing planks of about a metre and a half in length. A tree thus trained can produce a full crop of cork each time it is stripped. This type of pruning also includes control of the end branches to regulate their length, number, distribution and position. Training therefore takes place over three stages: first the formation of the trunk, secondly the selection of boughs after the extraction of the virgin cork and lastly the selection of branches immediately following the first extraction of reproduction cork.

After this gradual process the second layer of reproduction cork begins to form and the tree begins to produce acorns, signalling the oak's maturity. From this stage on, the aim of pruning will be to maintain or consolidate the tree, now that it has entered its most productive period, forming the best quality cork: not too thick, and consequently not very porous and relatively free from cracks in comparison with that produced by younger trees, nor too thin like the layers formed by old and aging trees. The aims of pruning during this period are fourfold. Firstly, correction of any end branches disfiguring the rounded shape of the crown, either vertically or horizontally. Secondly, hygiene, lopping any dry, diseased or aged branches, to stop them from harbouring plagues or becoming a stronghold of disease. Thirdly, thinning, to remove dense or intertwining branches which block out the light, and lastly, clipping the end branches of the crown, which causes the branches to shoot vigorously, to encourage the tree to bear flowers, and thus fruit.

Yellowing foliage and the absence of spring shoots, sometimes accompanied by the appearance of dried ends on branchlets, are incontrovertible signs that the cork oak is aging. It now needs to be revitalised and rebalanced. The basic requirement in these cases is the removal of a good number of branches, in order to reduce its need for nourishment by cutting down on the number of areas to feed, i.e., on the size of the crown. This will re-establish the balance between absorp-

AZULEJO PANEL
AT THE RAILWAY
STATION OF VILA
VIÇOSA,
DEPICTING CORK
BEING STRIPPED
FROM THE OAKS.

BELOW: THE
CORK STRIPPER'S
ESSENTIAL KIT:
CORK AXE,
PITCHER AND
COCHO.

tion through the roots and production of nutrients in the leaves.

CORK STRIPPING

This most delicate of operations is also the most consequential for the vitality of the cork oak. Suffice it to say that it is the most anti-natural operation which the tree undergoes, and so the most likely upset its internal balance. By removing the cork, the protective layer is stripped from the oak's most delicate organ, the inner bark, which serves as pipeline for the phloem sap whilst also being home to the two layers of cell division, the cambium and the phellogen.

Indeed, the phellogen marks the junction of the cork tissue with the inner bark, and it is from this point that the cork is removed in spring or summer. At this time of year the cork comes away easily from the trunk because the tree is growing and new cork cells being generated; these new cells are still tender and break easily.

When the cork has been stripped the phellogen and part of the inner bark die with time, and as a result some the phloem sap seeps to the outside surface. Cork stripping naturally leaves the oak somewhat debilitated.

Nonetheless, with its vast reserves of endurance in the face of adversity, the wounds generally heal at the end of three months and life returns to normal.

To keep the cork oak in good health and producing cork of a reasonable calibre and to avoid premature aging a minimum level of husbandry is required and, indeed, imposed by law. Virgin cork may not be removed from saplings until they have grown to a girth around the cork of 60 centimetres at chest height, and reproduction cork may not be extracted until the tree is at least 9 years old.

When stripping the cork, the utmost care must be taken not to damage the cambium which, unlike the phellogen, cannot regenerate itself. When wounded, it heals very slowly and

Cork
TRANSPORTED
THROUGH THE
FOREST TO BE
STACKED, DURING
TWO PERIODS IN
HISTORY (IN THE
PAST AND TODAY).

the wood may start to rot. Even when this is avoided, there is no escaping a permanent scar which will disfigure future cork planks and reduce their value.

Difficulties in cork stripping normally arise because the operation is not carried out when the tree is in full growth, and the new layer of suberose tissue is beginning to form, facilitating the removal of the cork. As soon as it is evident that the cork is being stripped too early or too late in the season the operation should be immediately brought to a halt, as a year's delay in cork extraction is to be preferred to lifelong mutilation of the oak.

It should always be remembered that stripping is extremely traumatic for the tree. For as long as the cork does not regenerate the cork oak is in peril of its life. It may even die, if soon after cork extraction the temperature rises too high or there is sustained rainfall.

Economic value

Regardless of the benefits which the cork oak brings to the ecosystems in which it lives and to cereal farming which shelters under its protection, it also provides many products of economic value.

Its incalculable value is all the greater when one considers its ability to thrive against the odds in areas where no other intensive forest species would survive. The cork oak is alone in turning these lands to advantage.

The value of the cork oak — and here we refer specifically to Portugal, where the cork oak adapted perfectly to very unproductive soils and supports an ecosystem unique in the world — should not be measured merely by the products extracted from the tree, but rather by the whole complex of agriculture, forestry, woodlands grazing and hunting which turns around the cultivation of this one tree.

ACORNS

The cork oak begins to bear fruit at between 15 and 20 years of age. But only when it reaches 30 or 40 does its production of acorns begin to be of economic interest. Fruit crop per unit of crown surface is at its highest in communities aged 50 to 150.

In Portugal, cork oak acorns, like those from sister species, are used almost exclusively for fattening swine. Fatstock being kept in the open air are allowed into the cork oak woods towards the end of October and leave, after fattening, towards the end of January. They normally put on 30 kilogrammes, but their are recorded cases where this figure rises to 100 kilogrammes.

Straw and acorns scattered on the ground provide food for fatstock born in spring and summer and for sheep.

African swine fever has had repercussions on the use of acorns for fattening swine over the last few decades. As a result, more has been turned over to the production of food oils and the manufacture of animal feeds.

WOOD

In days gone by, cork oak trunks were widely used in the golden age of ship building in the era of the Discoveries.

Today, their economic value is very limited. They are used only in the manufacture of simple agricultural tools (hoes and harrows), door frames and chimney beams, etc. Ships, alas, are no longer built from wood.

Though of the same family as the oak, the wood of the cork oak is of little value partly because it is difficult to work, but also because it often cracks while drying, making it less attractive as a material for furniture making or coopering.

ABOVE: ACORN,
FED TO SWINE.

BELOW: CORK
OAK SAPLING WITH
VERDANT FOLIAGE.

Branches pruned from cork oaks. The cork extracted *(falca)* is used in the manufacture of agglomerates.

Waste wood from the cork oak which can be put to various uses, such as the production of cellulose or charcoal.

FIREWOOD AND CHARCOAL

The smaller branches of the cork oak removed in pruning and thinning can be used as domestic fuel.

Charcoal production, however, is the most important, if not the only, end to which the wood of the cork oak is put.

Cork oak charcoal, at 25% humidity, has an absolute calorific value in the order of 7,000 calories.

At the end of the nineteenth century, the ashes of cork oak wood were found to be a source of potash. At the time, this was a profitable business, but it resulted in irreparable devastation to cork forests in Italy, Sardinia and Corsica.

CELLULOSE

Cellulose pulp from cork oak wood is much the same as that obtained from other trees. The quantity produced is likewise normal, 35 to 40% of the weight of soda-dried wood.

The fibres are small in size and the low length/width ratio reduces the resistance of the cross linkage for which reason cork cellulose should be used in sealing products.

Gradual decline in the use of charcoal made from cork oak wood has led to a rising uptake of the wood for paper pulp.

INNER BARK

The wood of the cork oak, notwithstanding its use in the production of cellulose, may likewise be given over to the extraction of tannin.

However, richer than the heartwood is the inner bark. The inner bark of adult cork oaks which have never been stripped for their cork has the highest content of tannate materials.

The demand from tanners of skins and hides led to the worldwide disappearance of centuries old cork oaks, once the pride of their native lands.

The fame of Morrocan leather can be traced, to a considerable extent, to the practice of tanning with the products of the inner bark of the cork oak. Such was the interest in this material that, principally in Morocco, cork oak forests suffered irreversible devastation at the end of the nineteenth and the beginning of the twentieth century.

Tannin from the inner bark of the cork oak was used in the slow tanning process. This was a major contributing factor to the decline in demand when fast tanning processes gained worldwide acceptance.

LEAVES

Branches and twigs removed in thinning and pruning is fed to both sheep and goats, although as forage it is of little value because the leaves are leathery and astringent.

New fallen leaves can be used for compost. Fermentation in ditches produces a product rich in potash with a reasonable content of nitrogen and phosphoric acid and a fertiliser content above that of dead leaves which have decomposed on the soil surface. In the latter case, significant losses of nitrogen and tertiary compounds (cellulose, fatty and pentosan substances) occur.

CORK

Cork is the main motivating factor behind all the care taken in the cultivation of the cork oak.

The foregoing sections are no more than the background for the detailed account which follows.

We shall focus here on only one point: the quantity of cork yielded by a healthy cork oak depends on the girth and height of its trunk, the number of boughs stripped for their cork and the height up to which they are stripped.

The world average for productivity, based on ten yearly extraction, is around 150 kilogrammes of cork per hectare.

But sources consulted show production in Portugal to stand at between 2,000 and 2,500 kilogrammes per hectare in large cork forests. Nor is it rare for the figure to climb to 5,000 kilogrammes, or even more. Cases are known of cork oaks aged between 35 and 40 years which yield 90 kilogrammes of cork, and of trees aged between 50 and 60 which can provide 150 kilogrammes of reproduction cork.

CORK STRIPPED FROM ONE TREE.

CORK

In the cultivation of the cork oak the prime aim is a high quantity, high quality yield. Cork is a raw material with a wide variety of applications in vast sectors such as the wine industry and throughout the construction industry.

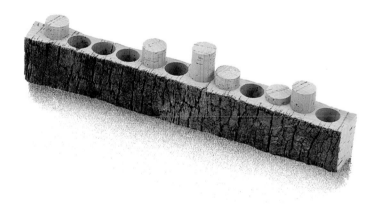

Characteristics

Cork is the name commonly given to the suber or suberose tissue formed by the phellogen of the cork oak.

It is a bark or protective shell which acts as the tree's epidermis.

STRUCTURE

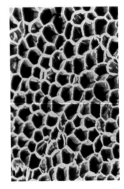

Cork is a plant (vegetable) tissue made up of dead micro--cells, generally 14-sided polyhedrons, slotting in one against the other, with the intercell space entirely filled with a gaseous mixture almost identical to air.

The suberose parenchyma is highly homogenous, consisting almost entirely of cellular membranes through which no channels run.

Although it clings to the tree, cork is a tissue formed of dead cells. The contents of newly formed cells disappears during growth and the subsequent process of suberisation of the membranes, on completion of which all communication with the plant's living tissues ceases.

The cork cell presents a minimal quantity of solid matter and a maximal quantity of gaseous matter, essentially atmospheric air but without the carbon dioxide.

The intra-cellular layers comprise five parts: two made of cellulose clad the cell chambers full of air, a further two of hard matter, impermeable to water (suberin and waxes), and a final part which is ligneous, whose function is to maintain the required structure and rigidity.

The cells are not arranged in uniform fashion. Although the appearance is that of a honeycomb, close examination that each of the cells is polygonal, but the number of sides varies between 4 and 8, and there are sometimes more.

Portuguese cork consists of mostly hexagonal cells, the form being that of an irregular solid with 14 sides.

But it is not only its honeycomb structure which gives cork such remarkable and advantageous characteristics. Many of these are due to the nature of the cellular membranes.

To give an idea of the size of cork cells suffice it to say that 1 cubic centimetre of suberose parenchyma contains somewhere around 40 million cells.

In cork, the thickness of the cellular membranes, practically constant in cells produced in spring and early summer (1 to 1.25 microns) gradually increases until the autumn, reaching 2 to 2.5 microns in the last cell layers formed before the phellogen goes dormant for the winter.

The cell height — measured diametrically between two tops — also fluctuates greatly: maximum values of 70 microns are reached in spring, and minimum values of around 10 microns in the last layer before the tree goes dormant in the Autumn.

Cell diameters, obviously, also vary, between 10 and 50 microns; the majority lie between 30 and 40 microns.

This unevenness, both in membrane thickness and in the height and diameter of the cell forming the suberose parenchyma, can affect some of the cork's mechanical and physical properties, namely its compressibility and elasticity.

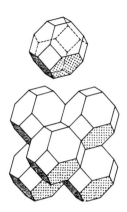

Top: POLYHEDRIC CELL PATTERN OF CORK.

Left-hand page. Top: SINGLE CELL FROM THE SUBEROSE TISSUE OF THE CORK OAK (CROSS SECTION).

Below: TANGENTIAL SECTION THROUGH CORK.

CHEMICAL COMPOSITION

The composition of cork may be broadly defined as follows: 45% suberin, 27% lignin, 12% cellulose and polysaccharides,

6% tannins, 5% waxes and 5% ash and other compounds.

All these elements have been extracted from cork since 1942, given their growing application in industry.

Cork is saponified by strong alkalis, and dissolved by nitric acid and halogenous oxidants.

VARIETY

Not all cork is the same. The range of diversity is broad, and is conditioned by a variety of factors which may be traced back to the cork oak forests or the hardships suffered by individual trees.

In terms simply of the life cycle of the cork oak, three qualities of suberose tissue are evident: virgin cork, reproduction cork from the second stripping and reproduction cork from subsequent strippings.

Virgin cork is the name given to the suberose tissue extracted first time round. Characteristically, it has a harder, more irregular structure. *Summer virgin (augment)* is the cork taken from part of the tree above the top level of the previous extraction. *Winter virgin (hatchet)* is the virgin cork from branches removed in pruning when extracted lengthwise, containing fragments of liber and ligneous tissue. The same cork, but extracted transversely is free of liber and ligneous tissue and is referred to as *winter virgin (adze)*.

The peripheral cells become meristematic and give rise to the phellogen. This layer soon asserts its own identity under the layer of epidermal cells.

The sapling's periderm only begins to form in the second year of life, and sometimes even waits until the fourth. By this time the suberose tissue is already fairly thick.

A particular feature of the phellogen is that once differentiated from neighbouring layers, it can stay active for the entire life of the tree.

THE DIFERENT
CORK TYPES:
I — VIRGIN,
2 — SECONDARY,
3 — AMADIA.

There exist records of an original phellogen which remained active for almost 150 years, which as a result consistently produced virgin cork.

But, with the exception of these extremely rare cases, the original phellogen is replaced by another in the phelloderm.

After extracting the summer virgin cork, in Portugal given the technical name *desbóia,* when the sapling has grown to a stem girth of at least 60 centimetres and a height of 1.20 metres (by which point it will be 25 to 30 years old), the new phellogen soon starts generating cork. The first of these layers, extracted after 9 years is given the name *secondary cork* and that produced from subsequent extraction *amadia.* The first layer of reproduction cork is more even than summer virgin cork, but cannot match the perfect quality of *amadia.*

The dead tissues of the inner bark, extraneous to the cork produced by the new phellogen, comprises the *rasp bark* or the backs of the future plank.

After stripping, the inner bark is pink and then gradually darkens in contact with the air: this is due to the oxidisation

of tannins. After a few months it sometimes turns a reddish black colour.

Rain discolours the rasp bark; by the time a new layer of cork is ready the rasp bark will have turned a greyish hue, especially on the side of the trunk most exposed to sun and bad weather.

The depth at which the new merismatic layer is differentiated in the inner bark, thereby determining the thickness of the rasp bark, has a certain bearing on some of the cork's characteristics, increasing or diminishing its commercial value.

The main difference between reproduction cork from the second and third extractions is, for example, that the former has much thicker rasp bark with transversal cracks.

Indeed, within the same tree the rasp bark is thinner the further up the tree; likewise the inner bark is thinner the further away it is from the soil.

AN ADULT TREE STANDS GUARD OVER A GROVE OF SAPLINGS.

With each successive extraction the thickness of the rasp bark and the inner bark decreases, and the porosity of the cork falls appreciably over the extraction of the first layers of the *amadia*.

Lenticular production is also related in part to the depth of the regeneration of the phellogen.

In thin inner bark, the lenticels of the periderm are smaller in diameter and less numerous per unit of surface than in thick inner barks.

The fact that the number and area of lenticels is so strongly dependent on the depth at which the phellogen is differentiated is most likely due to the influence exerted by this depth of regeneration on the exchange of gases between the liberine tissues and the exterior at the moment at which the new layer is formed.

When the phellogen is regenerated deep into the inner bark, impeding the access of air to the internal tissues, larger, more numerous lenticels are formed to overcome difficulties in breathing.

In conclusion, the bellies of the cork planks reproduce the contours of the inner bark surface.

The smoother and more homogenous the cork, and the denser the interior surface of the plank, the greater its commercial value.

CORK GROWTH AND AGE

The cork oak is an evergreen species, and so able to keep its physiological processes active at all times. Even so, the generating layers suspend their activity during the winter, the exact period of dormancy depending on environmental factors.

Consequently, the phellogen is only active for 6 or 7 months of the year.

The differences in cell size and the thickness of the cellular membrane between cork produced in spring and the succeding autumn leave discernible rings showing the extent of each year's growth.

Suberose tissue produced in the autumn has a darker colour than that of the spring.

Inside the rasp bark the first layer corresponds to growth from the regeneration of the phellogen until its annual activity came to a close towards the end of October.

This is where one starts when counting the age of the cork. After the rasp bark comes the first layer of soft, light coloured cork, bordered by the dark ring of the autumn production. This represents half a year's growth.

Eight annual layers then follow, finishing with another half layer on the belly of the plank, corresponding to the spring--summer period of the year in which the cork is extracted.

Nine year old cork thus has 9 autumn layers, 9 complete spring-summer layers and two half spring-summer layers (one inside the rasp bark, formed soon after the previous occasion when the tree was stripped, and another on the belly, which was still being formed when the tree was stripped).

The thickest suberose layer is generally that formed in the growing cycle subsequent to cork extraction.

From this point on, the quantity of cork produced diminishes progressively from year to year.

From the twentieth year of cork reproduction, however, the quantity of suberose tissue virtually levels off, with only the slightest reduction from year to year.

Exceptions to this rule can be traced to various reasons. Differences in the weather from one year to the next, especially changes in the rainfall pattern and the length of summer, poorly executed pruning or thinning, undue tillage of the soil, destruction of foliage by parasites or fire. All these factors can result in irregularities.

Physical and mechanical properties

The properties of cork derive naturally from the structure and chemical composition of the membranes.

It should be remembered that each cubic centimetre of cork's honeycomb structure contains between 30 and 42 million cells.

Because 89.7% of the tissue consists of gaseous matter, the density of cork is extremely low, in the order of 0.12 to 0.20, a fact which bears witness to the huge disproportion between the volume and the weight of the material.

LIGHTNESS

Cork is light and will float on water. For many thousands of years, this has been its most evident and most celebrated characteristic. In antiquity cork was used in fishing equipment. These properties are largely responsible for the esteem in which cork was held in Mediterranean civilisations from the most ancient times until the middle of the XVIII century.

ELASTICITY

The cellular membranes are very flexible, rendering the cork both compressible and elastic. In other words, it returns to its previous shape after being subjected to pressure. These characteristics, in alliance with others, largely explain how cork has become indispensable for stoppers.

This capacity means that the cork can be fitted perfectly against the walls of the bottle neck. When cork is subjected to strong pressure the gas in the cells is compressed and reduces considerably in volume. When released from pressure cork immediately recovers its original volume and bears no trace of having been subjected to any appreciable deformation.

IMPERMEABILITY

The presence of suberin (a complex mixture of fatty acids and heavy organic alcohols) renders cork impermeable to both liquids and gases. As a result it does not rot, and may therefore be considered the best seal in existence. The presence of tannins and the scarcity of albuminoids makes it even more effective; cork may thus be considered to have no tendency whatsoever to rot and to be wholly unaltered by humidity. Pieces of cork exist which were submerged underwater for centuries on end without rotting.

LOW CONDUCTIVITY

The value of cork is further increased by its low conductivity of either heat, sound or vibrations. This is due to the fact that the gaseous elements is sealed in tiny, impervious compartments, insulated one from the other by a moisture resistant material of low specific gravity. Cork has consequently one of the best insulating capacities of all natural substances.

RESISTANCE TO WEAR

Cork is also remarkable resistant to wear and has a high friction coefficient, thanks to the honeycomb structure of the suberose surface.

It also boasts other qualities. It does not absorb dust and consequently does not cause allergies nor pose a risk to asthma sufferers, it is constitutionally inalterable and so its efficiency is guaranteed, it is fire resistant, making it a natural fire retardant, etc.

This host of incontrovertible qualities, allied to poor conductivity, be it of heat or sound, combine to make cork an increasingly sought after material in the most advanced techniques of construction of all kinds of buildings.

THE PROCESS FOR
SELECTING AND
PREPARING CORK
IS PRACTICALLY
UNCHANGED: IN
THE PAST (LEFT)
AND TODAY
(ABOVE).

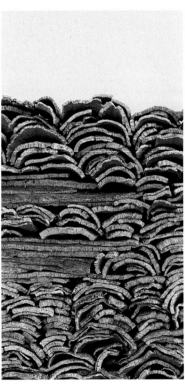

Characteristics useful for different purposes

It is not strictly correct to speak in isolation of the qualities and unsuitability or defects of cork. Both positive and negative properties should be examined in terms of the objectives proposed in the different applications of the material.

What is an advantage for one manufactured product might well be a disadvantage to be taken into consideration in the production of a different material in which cork is incorporated.

Thus if the cork is too porous or hard, for example, as well as insufficiently or excessively elastic, certain cork planks may be considered unsuitable for stopper production, there is no serious obstacle to their being sent for grinding. On the other hand, planks with knots or tiny scales of sclerenchyma are not suitable for processing into agglomerated cork. Although the stopper industry takes these considerations into account, it still uses these planks.

So it is not possible to make broad statements about the «defects» of cork, but only to discuss specific characteristics which affect the homogeneity of the material and its physical, chemical and mechanical properties.

POROSITY

It is one of cork's singular features that it is permeable to air. This is not a consequence of the honeycomb structure of the cells but rather of the lenticels, orifices or pores in the tissue.

In restricted, more or less circular, patches the phellogen, in addition to normal suberose cells, also produces a limp tissue of rounded cells whose membranes are not subsequently suberised. The purpose of these cells is to allow gases to be

exchanged between the living tissues of the cork oak and the exterior atmosphere.

The lenticels render the cork porous. The porosity depends not on the number of pores or lenticels on the surface of the corkwood plank, but instead on the area occupied by lenticular channels in pieces of cork cut tangentially.

Cork's natural porosity may at times be excessive. The number, and above all, the diameter of the lenticular channels in Portuguese cork are one of the reasons for its great economic value.

Cork is considered not very porous with values less than 2%, to present average porosity when they lie between 2 and 4% and high porosity when over 4%. When porosity is above 6% the cork is referred to as *lung*.

Some cork is referred to as *earthy (barrenta* or *terrenta)* when it is characterised by a special type of porosity. The name comes from the brownish, reddish or earth coloured powdered material filling the lenticular channels, due to an aberration in the suberose generating layer which occurs in restricted areas and during part of the cork formation period.

DENSITY

Density is the relation between the mass of a body and the volume it fills. Cork normally has a low density, which lies behind two of its more evident qualities: lightness and the ability to float.

The density varies on the whole between 0.12 and 0.20. But planks are occacionally found with a specific gravity much higher than normal, sometimes as high as that of the rytidome of other quercus species such as the oak.

Unusually high density is due to either the breadth of the liberine rays which form very thick walls, in turn forming *cortiça preguenta,* or the presence of sclerenchyma and liberine or phellodermic tissues in the cork, which is referred to as *woody* cork.

If the cork is too dense is will be hard and unsuitable for the stopper industry where the right degree of elasticity is a prerequisite. It may, however, be put to other uses where its physical and mechanical properties will be welcome.

Application

Cork needs to be treated to be properly applied in industry. Cork in its raw form is only used in traditional, pre-industrial products, such as beehives and roofing for traditional dwellings.

When planks have been cut from the cork oaks, they are sorted to separate any which might not be suitable for any of the many profitable uses to which they can be put. They are then piled up and left in the open air for six months. The rain, sun and wind trigger various chemical transformations in cork which improve its quality.

They are then layered in huge boilers with boiling water for 75 minutes. The aim of this operation is to remove any animal flora from the forest, to extract contaminating products and to render the planks softer and more flexible.

After boiling they are piled up again and left for about three weeks, during which time they become smoother and the cellular structure becomes easier to work.

The corkwood planks are then sorted into quality grades. The best cork goes to stopper production and the remainder is used for agglomerates.

Depending on whether the intention is to use cork with or without other elements (rubber, cement, etc.) the planks are first cut into sections or granulated.

It the aim is to extract chemical products contained in the cork tissue, the technique used is as follows: the cork is saponified in a hot solution of caustic soda, then acidified with sulphuric acid which releases the fatty acids and their soda compounds. Finally the fatty acids are separated from the ligneous tissue by using solvents (trichloroethylene, alcohol, etc.).

SCIENTIFIC RESEARCH IN A MODERN UNIT BELONGING TO THE AMORIM GROUP.

A WIDE RANGE OF USES

As was pointed out above, cork has been used in fishing tackle, as stoppers for vases and for domestic purposes since time immemorial.

In 1680, the French benedictine monk Dom Pierre Pérignon discovered the effectiveness of a cork stopper in receptacles for sparkling wine (champagne). In so doing, he reopened a huge domain to the use of cork in the wine sector, a process which gathered pace when glass bottles came into general use.

Towards the end of the XIX century, however, cork oak

ISOLATED ADULT
CORK OAK. IN THE
BACKGROUND, A
WIDE AREA OF
CORK FOREST.

farming began to face a gloomier future. The cork stopper began to be replaced by other sealing processes, less suitable for their purpose, and cheaper and more attractive. Declining demand for cork undermined the profitability of cork oak farming; it should be remembered that only 25% of cork is suitable material for stopper production.

It was at this point, in 1891, that an American, John Smith, accidentally discovered the possibility of producing a cork agglomerate. This reopened the horizons of cork oak farming, as all cork produced could be put to full use.

Agglomerated cork retains all its properties, and being unaltered by contact with oil, fats and petrol it soon found a multiplicity of uses such as few other materials could boast.

Until 1942, cork was exploited only for its exceptional physical and mechanical properties, in other words, those qualities by reason of which it lends itself so well to stoppers and agglomerates.

But the range of uses to which cork could be put expanded as from this date when chemical components began to be extracted from cork tissue. Ligneous products, properly treated, yield a plastic material used in mouldings for electrical material. The stable emulsions obtained with hard wax are prized in the manufacture of chemical paper, polishes, paraffin treatments for fruit, plastics, records, varnishes, paints and soaps. Suberonyl can be transformed by hot polymerisation into a resinous gum used in the production of varnishes with excellent adherence to metals (copper and aluminium); foionic acid is used in the manufacture of musk scented perfumes and of nylon-type plastics.

Cork tissue is used in two basic forms: treated cork planks and ground cork.

Corkwood planks are used to manufacture a great many products: stoppers, bungs, washers, buoys, carpets and floor coverings, facings for walls and ceilings, inner soles, records, polishing blocks, protector plates and a wide range of handi-

CORK STOPPERS
AND CHAMPAGNE
THE PERFECT
MARRIAGE.

ABOVE: AN
OPERATION IN
STOPPER
MANUFACTURE.

BELOW: STOPPERS
IN BOTTLES AT A
WINE PRODUCTION
UNIT.

elasticity, safeguarding a completely hermetic seal to the receptacle it serves.

A cork stopper thus conserves the wine's individual qualities and allows it to improve with age.

If wine is occasionally «corked», this is mostly due to factors other than the cork.

Sparkling wine is a case in point. Here a cork is irreplaceable, being the only material which can be fashioned into a suitable stopper, a specially designed type of cork to maintain the gas pressure in the bottle and to stop the gas escaping. The lower part of the cork, in this case, consists of discs of natural cork glued one to the other. The upper part, also known as the «head» or «body», is made from cork granules. The most modern technique is individual moulding, where the granules are submitted to uniform pressure.

These same discs are also produced in a much smaller size for use in bottles for beer, water, soft drinks and water.

USE OF AGGLOMERATES...

If the cork stopper is the most ancient use of cork, dating back thousands of years, the use of agglomerated cork can claim a history of exactly one century, having been initiated in 1891.

The numerous unequalled characteristics of the raw material, in terms of comfort, make of agglomerated cork a product in vigorous expansion, used greatly in construction, the automobile and electrical industries, shipbuilding, metalomechanics and petrochemicals.

There are two categories of agglomerated cork. In *pure expanded agglomerates,* the granules are aglutinated with the cork oak's own resins with heat treatment under pressure.

In *compound agglomerates,* granulated cork is aglutinated with non-cork oak products such as asphalt, rubber, casein,

TRADITIONAL
PROCESS FOR
EXTRACTING *FALCA*
CORK. TODAY
MECHANICAL
PROCESSES ARE
USED.

TRADITIONAL
PROCESS FOR
EXTRACTING *FALCA*
CORK. TODAY
MECHANICAL
PROCESSES ARE
USED.

cement, gypsum, glue, plastic, natural or synthetic resins, etc. There are thus many possibilities, depending on the end is view.

... *in bottling*

The body or head of corks for champagne and sparkling wine are, as stated, made of cork agglomerate. Although the most common production technique is individual moulding, extrusion and block production are also possible.

Corks for normal table wine, cider and some types of beer are also made from 100% cork agglomerate.

Cork agglomerate discs are also produced and have similar uses to those of natural cork discs.

... in interior decoration

In recent years, architects and designers have rediscovered the beauty of many natural materials in both their raw and finished states. This has led to a wider use of cork, in a range of tones and textures, in different jobs for different moods. Nowadays, the use of cork in decoration is rising in popularity, not only among professionals, but also among diy enthusiasts.

Cork, as a natural product, warms and enriches any interior. It can be used on the floor, on the walls or on the ceiling, and now comes is a wide range of colours, from its familiar honey tones to green, red, chocolate or nearly black.

Cork always blends in well with other decorations and with any sort of furniture. Rightly valued for its visual appeal, its functional side is also very attractive. In addition to giving thermal and sound insulation, it only needs minimal maintenance.

Flooring tiles are produced from cork granules aglutinated with synthetic resins under heat and pressure.

There are tiles of all thicknesses, densities and finishes: just polished, waxed, varnished, urethaned, or vinyl-coated. This last group can be produced in a wide range of models, using a decorative sheet between the transparent PVC and the agglomerate underneath. The use of silk screen printing has made the range of decorative possibilities still wider.

Cork tile pavements are quiet, warm and comfortable. Being highly abrasion resistant, they are often used in all sorts of public buildings including schools, hospitals, shops, offices, museums, libraries, airports, hotels and restaurants. The distinctive look and durability of cork tiles make them the perfect choice.

In the home, cork tiles can be happily incorporated all over the house. Their resistance to humidity and their non-slip surface make them especially suitable for the kitchen and the

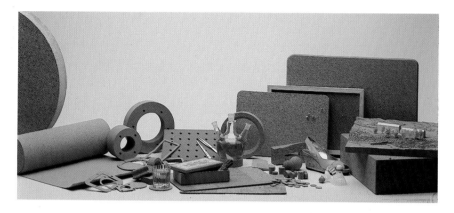

ABOVE: RANGE OF
PRODUTS MADE
FROM CORK.

BELOW: ONE OF THE MAIN
USES OF CORK:
FLOORING.

bathroom, while they are a luxurious and long-lasting alternative for the living room and bedrooms.

There is a wide variety of tiles and decorative panels. These can be made of natural cork sheets or agglomerate, and can be their original colour or have coloured designs added.

Cork wallpaper is made of thin sheets of cork glued on to coloured backing paper. The wide variety of possible bases means that there is an enormous range of products available.

Continuous rolls of decorative cork are used in the same way as the paper. Being thicker, they are recommended for heavy duty use.

... in building

The construction industry uses cork for a variety of purposes — thermal and sound insulation, in expansion and compression joints in concrete structures, to reduce wear and to eliminate vibrations.

In recent years, the increase in the price of oil and its derivatives has brought an increase in the use of cork as a means of saving energy. An air cushion is one of the most efficient means of insulation known. Cork, with its cellular structure where air is a major component, offers a high level of thermal insulation. Consequently, a large percentage of Portugal's annual production is used to make expanded cork agglomerate, which is also known as expanded agglomerate or black agglomerate.

CORK IS ALSO USED IN EVERYDAY OBJECTS.

This agglomerate is made from cork granules of various sizes, but of a larger size than that used in the production of floor tiles. The particles are bonded with their own resin in moulds using pressure and super-heated steam. The blocks are then cut into planks which are then finished as required.

These days, expanded cork agglomerate is widely used as insulation in roofs, walls, floors and ceilings. When, for example, it is used as a floating floor between two concre-

*ABOVE AND
BELOW:* CORK
USED IN
FLOORING.

RIGHT PAGE:
CORK USED IN
EXPANSION JOINTS:
BRIDGES,
BUILDINGS,
MOTORWAYS AND
DAMS.

te floors, the expanded agglomerate acts simultaneously as thermal insulation and to reduce noise between the two levels.

As it maintains its properties at very low temperatures, expanded agglomerate has a wide range of uses in the refrigeration industry. These include the construction of cold-rooms, insulating storage tanks and lagging for pipes carrying water or other liquids, at both very high and very low temperatures.

Expanded agglomerate maintains its insulating properties almost indefinitely in all these uses. Furthermore, it is extremely fire resistant, does not corrode and can bear heavy loads.

In addition to these exceptional properties, expanded agglomerate does not give off chloride, cyanide or any other toxic gases when burnt. It is the perfect insulation, as it has properties that no other form of insulation can claim: it offers the lowest level of heat conduction among fire resistant insulators and simultaneously the highest elasticity of the highly heat resistant.

Yet another use of cork in the construction industry is as expansion or compression joints in concrete structures, including dams and tunnels. In these cases, various types of compound agglomerates are used, while others are used to absorb vibration in buildings with metal structures.

... in leisure activities

Cork plays a large part in the fields of sport and leisure activities. For centuries, it has been an essential part in the production of fishing tackle. Cork buoys have been used in fishing nets since Biblical times, and the handles of fishing rods and floats and boxes for fishing equipment are all made of cork.

Cork is also used in safety helmets, life-jackets and life--buoys.

Hockey, golf and cricket balls, as well as baseballs and

This page: pure
expanded
agglomerate.

Right:
Diagram
showing the use
of pure
expanded
agglomerate in
outside walls.

Use of cork in
roofs.

Cork used for
conveying fluids
at extreme
temperatures
(from $-180°C$ to
$+100°C$).

shuttlecocks often include cork components, as do table tennis bats, the pea in whistles, golf clubs, dartboards, fireworks and bungs for gun cartridges.

Due to its attractive appearance and its pleasant feel, cork is also used in the production of gifts and novelties, such as engraved boxes, pictures and memoboards. Some of the other products which use cork are mats and coasters for plates and glasses, bath-mats, cigarette boxes, desk pads, ashtrays, and calendars. Cork, in combination with other products, specifically leather, is also used in a wide range of products such as handbags, travelling cases, wallets, purses, document holders, and, more recently, cloth for the clothing industry.

... and in technology

Although many natural raw materials have been replaced by man-made substitutes, cork is more and more an essential in modern industry.

The automobile, electrical, engineering and aeronautic industries are among the main consumers, and new uses are always being found for this incredibly versatile material which has served man since time immemorial.

Perhaps the most exciting development in the use of cork has been as the protective heat shield in missiles and space--craft, including the Space Shuttle.

In this case, the aim is to protect the rocket against the extremely high temperatures caused by friction on re-entry into the Earth's atmosphere.

Fire retardant cork agglomerate is used in warships, allowing highly efficient insulation of steam pipes and ventilation equipment. Its flexibility and low weight also make it the most efficient material for insulating pipes in small spaces. No other material can offer such good insulation in such a small space. In addition, it has been used in the internal lining of submarines.

The fact that cork is slow-burning and its property of ener-

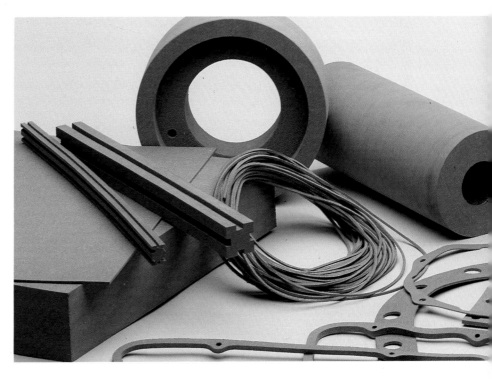

CORK WITH
RUBBER FLOORING
AND JOINTS IN
THE AUTOMOBILE
INDUSTRY, SHIP
BUILDING,
ELECTRIC AND
METAL MECHANICS
INDUSTRIES.

gy absorption make it a good means of transporting radio-active isotopes. The risk of radiation contamination after damage to the isotope container requires the use of a special covering which is highly heat resistant. The isotopes are placed in a small container which is then placed in a larger one. To ensure complete protection, the outer container is lined with cork.

As cork floats, natural cork is used in oil and petrol level indicators, but its most important use in the car industry is in cork/rubber gaskets. Nowadays, these gaskets are as essential as petrol or diesel for the automobile and truck industry. The materials used combine the compressibility and elasticity of cork with rubber's mechanical resistance and stability of size. This makes them the most suitable gaskets for oil tanks, the cylinder head, carburettor and gearbox.

The cork/rubber combination is easy to cut and, due to its flexibility and resistance, it can be used for gaskets with very narrow borders.

The electrical industry has also developed cork/rubber products to stop leaks of the fluids used in modern transformers.
Similar products are also used in the manufacture of electrical
switches, lightning rods and other transmission equipment, in
addition to conductor wires and washing machine lids.

The majority of machines cause vibrations. Not only does
this create bad working conditions, the vibrations can spread
to other machines or even to the building itself, frequently
leading to an intolerable atmosphere. High density expanded
agglomerate planks are the cheapest, easiest and most efficient means of insulating machines and damping vibrations.
Consequently, working conditions are improved, the machi-
nery's life expectancy is increased and the risk of costly structural damage is avoided.

Composition agglomerate of cork and rubber used for
pavements combines properties of having high resistance
to wear, being non-slip and sound absorbant. It is resis-

ABOVE: GASKET
INSTALLATION ON
CYLINDER HEAD.

RIGHT: USE OF
CORK IN
SHUTTLECOCKS.

tant to oil, grease and salt water, which makes it suitable for industrial and vehicle flooring. Buses, carriages, taxis, ships, gymnasiums, laboratories and factory floors are just some of the places where it is normally used, either in the form of the whole floor covering or in non-slip industrial nats.

In laboratory areas, cork is ideal as a base for the protection of work surfaces, in entomology and dissection, in support rings for bottles and for special stoppers.

There are innumerable other uses for cork; the ceramic industry uses discs to smooth rough edges and eliminate defects; it is used in small clutch linings; for polishing diamonds;

as a stopper in organ pipes and as mutes in wind instruments; for the cylinders in packaging machines when using waxed paper or cellulose film; in bathroom fittings, filling for mattresses and cushions; as a backing sheet for sandpaper. In these and other ways, cork is increasingly indispensable in today's industry.

Thanks to their superb properties, cork products have entered our everyday lives, as is illustrated by the following figures on world consumption:
— Natural cork stoppers for wine: 23 billion.
— Stoppers for champagne and sparkling wine: 1.5 billion.
— Pure expanded agglomerate: 150,000 m^3.
— Floor tiles: 10 million m^2.

Portugal, as we have said, leads the world in this field, possessing 30% of the total area of cork forest, producing more than 50% of total cork output and as home to 65% of the cork industry.

BIBLIOGRAPHY

Artigas, P., *Alcornocales y industria corchera*, Madrid 1907

Casquilho, Jorge, *A Propósito da Cortiça. Da Árvore à Garrafa*, Lisbon 1990

Camus, A., *Les Chênes. Monographie du genre "Quercus"*, Paris 1936

Faubel, A.L., *Cork and the American Cork Industry*, New York 1938

Giacobbe, A., *La sughera. Cultura-utilizzazione*, Casale Monferrato 1923

Giglioli, I., *Lo stato italiano e la cultura del sughero specialmente in Sardegna*, Portici 1902

Klauber, A., *Die Monographie des Korkes*, Berlin 1920

Kügler, K.F., *Über das Suberin*, Halle 1884

Lamey, A., *Le chêne-liège, sa culture et son exploitation*, Paris 1892

Marangoni, L., *Il sughero e la sua economia*, Mailand 1937

Martignat, M., *Le liège. Ses produits et ses sous-produits*, Paris 1905

Medrano, L.V. e Ugarte, J., *El alcornoque y el corcho*, Madrid 1922

Natividade, J.Vieira, *Subericultura*, Lisbon 1950

Palmgren, E., *Production et commerce international du liège*, Rome 1947

Santos, J.Brito dos, *ABC do Podador de Sobreiros e do Tirador de Cortiça*, Lisbon 1964

Schmidt, Ana, *Cortiça e Artigos de Cortiça*, Lisbon 1983

Thomas, P.E., *Cork Insulation*, Chicago 1928

PHOTOGRAPHIC CREDITS
A. Sequeira: cover, flyleaves, 2, 6, 9, 12-13, 17, 18, 21, 23, 24, 32, 33, 38, 39, 44-45, 48, 50, 53, 55, 56, 58-59, 61, 63, 66, 67, 72, 75, 80-81, 84-85, 86, 87, 88, 89, 91, 93, 94, 95, 98b, 99, 100-101, 103, 105, 106, 107, 124b, 126-127, 133-134, 135, 141. Centro de Arte Moderna da Fundação Calouste Gulbenkian: 41. Resource and Marketing Office of Grupo Amorim: 22a, 28, 29, 30, 31, 42, 43, 93a, 98a, 109, 115, 116, 124a, 125, 131, 137, 138, 139, 140, 144, 145, 146-147, 148, 149, 150, 151, 153, 154, 155. Instituto Português do Património Cultural; 38, 39. João Francisco Vilhena: 19a. Maurício Abreu: 14, 19, 20-21, 36-37, 76-77, 120-121, 129, 140. Museu Nacional de Arte Antiga: 27. Penaguião & Burnay: 68-69, 112-113.

ACKNOWLEDGEMENTS
We wish to thank the following institutions and individuals, who kindly gave their permission for photographs to be reproduced or used in this volume: Centro de Arte Moderna of the Fundação Calouste Gulbenkian (Lisbon), Museu do Mar (Cascais), Museu Nacional de Arte Antiga (Lisbon) and José Dórdio (Oporto).

INDEX

INTRODUCTION

PORTUGAL, THE CORK OAK'S ADOPTED HOME

THE CORK OAK

CORK

BIBLIOGRAPHY

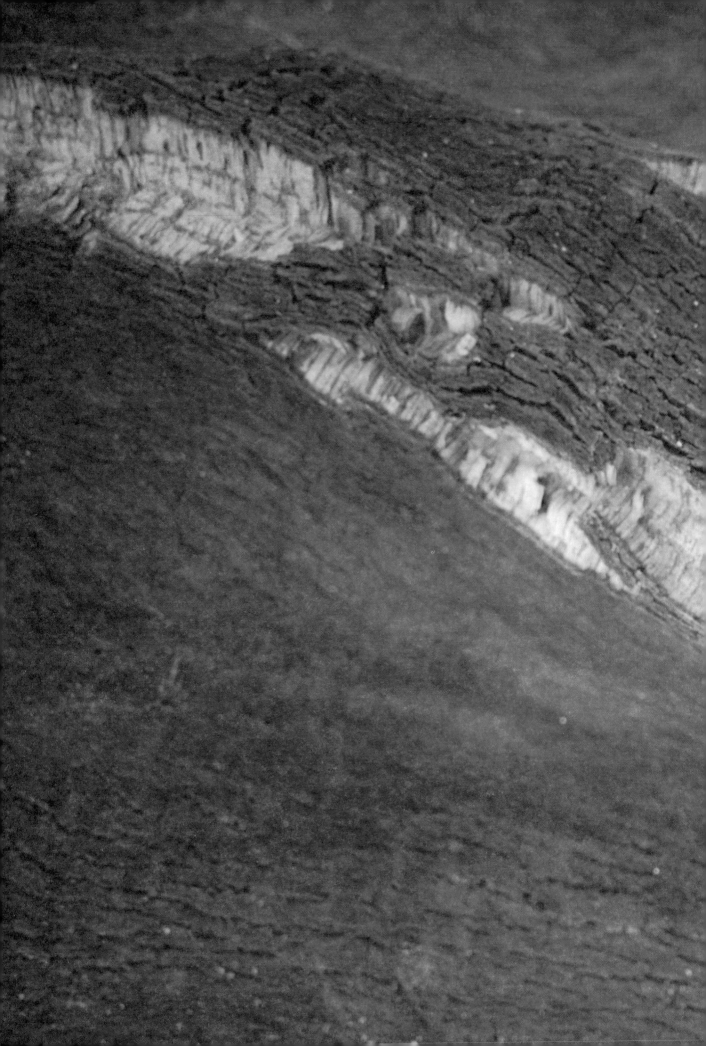